Life of Pi

by
Yann Martel

Student Packet

Written by
James H Duncan

Contains masters for:

- 2 Prereading Activities
- 7 Vocabulary Activities
- 1 Study Guide
- 3 Character Analysis Activities
- 2 Comprehension Activities
- 3 Literary Analysis Activities
- 7 Quizzes
- 1 Novel Test

PLUS Detailed Answer Key and Scoring Rubric

Teacher Note

Selected activities, quizzes, and test questions in this Novel Units® Student Packet are labeled with the appropriate reading/language arts skills for quick reference. These skills can be found above quiz/test questions or sections and in the activity headings.

Note

The 2004 Harcourt paperback edition of the novel, © 2001 by Yann Martel, was used to prepare this guide. The page references may differ in other editions. Novel ISBN: 0-15-603020-9

Please note: This novel deals with sensitive, mature issues. Parts may contain graphic descriptions of violence (including murder, the slaughtering of animals, and references to cannibalism). Please assess the appropriateness of this book for the age level and maturity of your students prior to reading and discussing it with them.

ISBN 978-1-60878-111-9

To order, contact your local school supply store, or—

Novel Units, Inc.
P.O. Box 97
Bulverde, TX 78163-0097

Web site: novelunits.com

Note to the Teacher

Selected activities, quizzes, and test questions in this Novel Units® Student Packet are labeled with the following reading/language arts skills for quick reference. These skills can be found above quiz/test questions or sections and in the activity headings.

Basic Understanding: The student will demonstrate a basic understanding of written texts. The student will:

- use a text's structure or other sources to locate and recall information (Locate Information)
- determine main idea and identify relevant facts and details (Main Idea and Details)
- use prior knowledge and experience to comprehend and bring meaning to a text (Prior Knowledge)
- summarize major ideas in a text (Summarize Major Ideas)

Literary Elements: The student will apply knowledge of literary elements to understand written texts. The student will:

- analyze characters from a story (Character Analysis)
- analyze conflict and problem resolution (Conflict/Resolution)
- recognize and interpret literary devices (flashback, foreshadowing, symbolism, simile, metaphor, etc.) (Literary Devices)
- consider characters' points of view (Point of View)
- recognize and analyze a story's setting (Setting)
- understand and explain themes in a text (Theme)

Analyze Written Texts: The student will use a variety of strategies to analyze written texts. The student will:

- identify the author's purpose (Author's Purpose)
- identify cause and effect relationships in a text (Cause/Effect)
- identify characteristics representative of a given genre (Genre)
- interpret information given in a text (Interpret Text)
- make and verify predictions with information from a text (Predictions)
- sequence events in chronological order (Sequencing)
- identify and use multiple text formats (Text Format)
- follow written directions and write directions for others to follow (Follow/Write Directions)

Critical Thinking: The student will apply critical-thinking skills to analyze written texts. The student will:

- write and complete analogies (Analogies)
- find similarities and differences throughout a text (Compare/Contrast)
- draw conclusions from information given (Drawing Conclusions)
- make and explain inferences (Inferences)
- respond to texts by making connections and observations (Making Connections)
- recognize and identify the mood of a text (Mood)
- recognize an author's style and how it affects a text (Style)
- support responses by referring to relevant aspects of a text (Support Responses)
- recognize and identify the author's tone (Tone)
- write to entertain, such as through humorous poetry or short stories (Write to Entertain)
- write to express ideas (Write to Express)
- write to inform (Write to Inform)
- write to persuade (Write to Persuade)
- demonstrate understanding by creating visual images based on text descriptions (Visualizing)
- practice math skills as they relate to a text (Math Skills)

Name ______________________

Getting the "Lay of the Land"

Directions: Prepare for reading by answering the following short-answer questions.

1. Who is the author?

   ____

2. What does the title suggest to you about the book?

   ____

3. When was the book first copyrighted?

   ____

4. How many pages are there in the book?

   ____

5. Thumb through the book. Read three pages—one from near the beginning, one from near the middle, and one from near the end. What predictions can you make about the book?

   ____

6. What does the cover suggest to you about the book?

   ____

Name ______________________________

Anticipation Guide

Directions: Rate each of the following statements before you read the novel, and discuss your ratings with a partner. After you have completed the novel, rate and discuss the statements again.

1 ——— 2 ——— 3 ——— 4 ——— 5 ——— 6
strongly agree | strongly disagree

	Before	After
1. You cannot belong to more than one religion at the same time.	_____	_____
2. Every story, no matter how truthful, has an element of invention or fantasy.	_____	_____
3. Learning to trust strangers in dire times is essential to survival.	_____	_____
4. Unlike humans, tigers hate the water and cannot swim.	_____	_____
5. False hope can sometimes serve a purpose.	_____	_____
6. A nickname only sticks when someone else gives it to you.	_____	_____
7. The ocean is like a desert—there is nothing to eat or drink.	_____	_____
8. A person always wants what s/he doesn't have.	_____	_____
9. It is foolish to believe something exists if you have never seen it.	_____	_____
10. It is better to botch a goodbye than a first impression.	_____	_____

Name ______________________________

Vocabulary Synonyms

anecdotes	exemplary	indolence	yogis
anemic	incessant	raiments	proffered
tremulous	intuitive	disrepute	strenuous

Directions: Choose the word or phrase closest in meaning to the vocabulary word as it is used in the novel. Then, on a separate sheet of paper, use at least four of the words in a brief analysis of Pi's childhood.

____ 1. **anecdotes:** (a) tales (b) tribes (c) troubles (d) truths

____ 2. **exemplary:** (a) meddling (b) meditative (c) misconstrued (d) model

____ 3. **indolence:** (a) lenience (b) lesson (c) lethargy (d) liability

____ 4. **yogis:** (a) teachers (b) theories (c) thoughts (d) tourists

____ 5. **anemic:** (a) fearful (b) feeble (c) fervent (d) festering

____ 6. **incessant:** (a) relentless (b) repentant (c) restrained (d) revolting

____ 7. **raiments:** (a) garments (b) gripes (c) grooves (d) guides

____ 8. **proffered:** (a) gambled (b) given (c) greeted (d) grizzled

____ 9. **tremulous:** (a) narrow (b) nervous (c) neutral (d) nurturing

____10. **intuitive:** (a) informal (b) injured (c) innocent (d) instinctive

____11. **disrepute:** (a) disgrace (b) disillusionment (c) dissatisfaction (d) distance

____12. **strenuous:** (a) tempting (b) tenacious (c) tender (d) tiring

Name ______________________________

Word Map

sanctified	intolerable	avatar	petulant
exaltation	askance	apoplectic	esplanade
depravity	precarious	memorabilia	incredulous

Directions: Complete the word map below for five of the vocabulary words above.

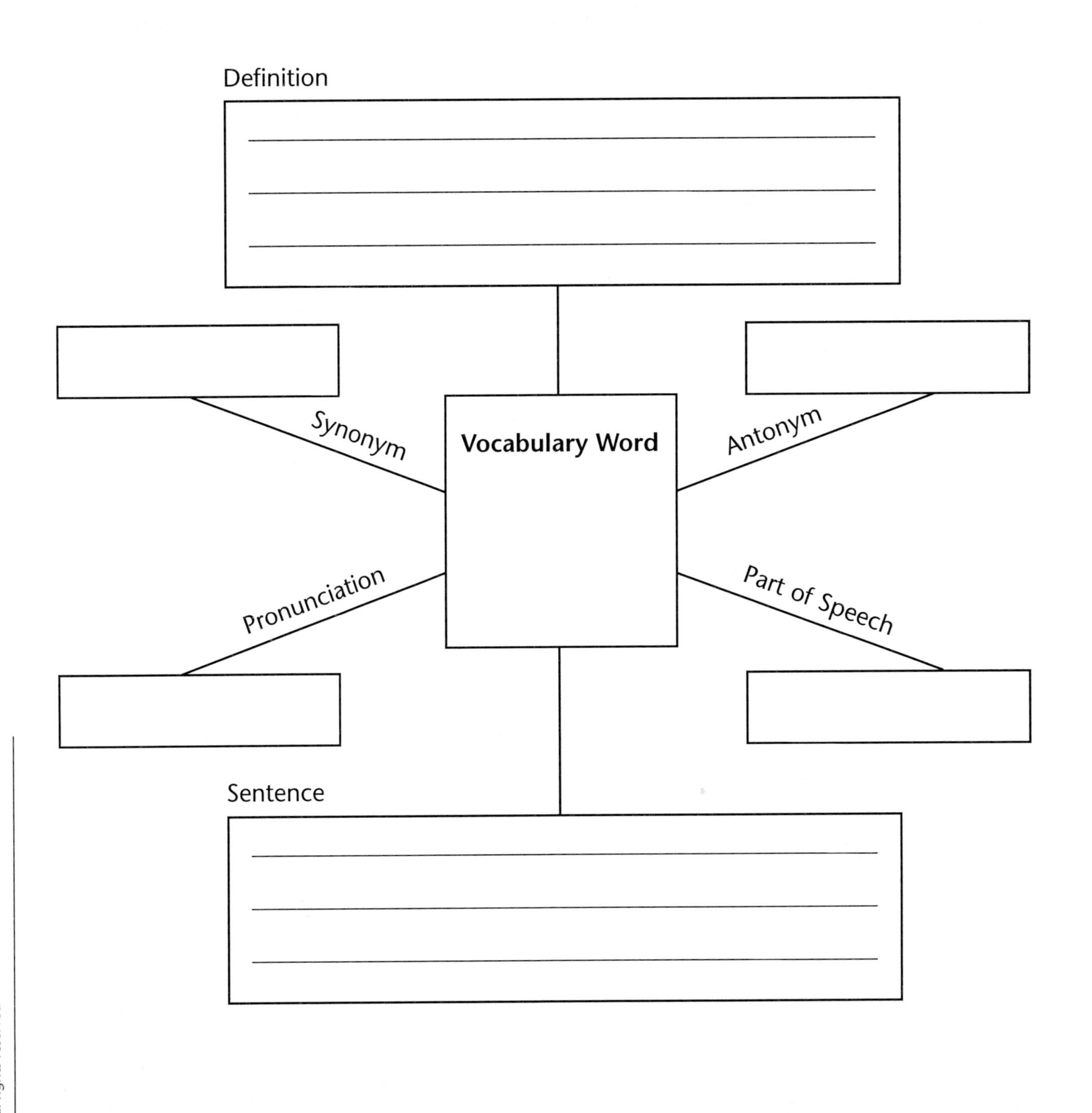

Name ______________________________

Vocabulary Sentence Sets

dyspeptic	ensconced	flotsam	aversion
dishevelled	remonstrations	empathy	abomination
empirical	supplication	catchment	

Directions: Write the vocabulary words from the list above on the numbered lines below.

1. ______________________________ 2. ______________________________
3. ______________________________ 4. ______________________________
5. ______________________________ 6. ______________________________
7. ______________________________ 8. ______________________________
9. ______________________________ 10. ______________________________
11. ______________________________

On a separate sheet of paper, use each of the following sets of words in an original sentence. Your sentences should show that you know the meanings of the vocabulary words as they are used in the story.

Sentence 1: words 8 and 4
Sentence 2: words 9 and 3
Sentence 3: words 10 and 2
Sentence 4: words 1 and 7
Sentence 5: words 5 and 2
Sentence 6: words 6 and 3
Sentence 7: words 2 and 1
Sentence 8: words 5 and 11
Sentence 9: words 7 and 9
Sentence 10: words 10 and 8

Name ______________________________

Newspaper

lucidity	lithesome	attrition	mantra
unerring	brackish	galleon	evanescent
sentient	sanguinary	mutinous	

Directions: Imagine you are a tabloid reporter writing a story explaining why the *Tsimtsum* sank. Use the vocabulary words above to write a creative, unique, and outlandish tabloid story about the ship's sinking. Continue on another sheet of paper if necessary.

Weird World News

Wednesday, October 2 • Section A, Page 1

____

____

____

____

____

____

____

____

____

____

____

____

____

____

____

Name ______________________________

Vocabulary Crossword

tilaks	translucent	forbearance	misconstrue
malaise	pendulum	gregarious	hillocks
archipelago	heinous	exalted	

Across

4. patience; self-control
6. to get the wrong impression; to misunderstand
8. Hindu marks worn on the forehead as symbols of the divine
9. lifted up; glorious; most holy
10. social and unreserved
11. a hanging weight that swings back and forth in a timed pattern

Down

1. see-through; transparent
2. shockingly evil or wicked
3. a series of small hills
5. a chain of islands
7. listless state; state of depression

Name ______________________________

Life of Pi
Activity #8 • Vocabulary
Chapters 87–93

Synonym or Antonym?

emaciated	infernal	sacrilegious	amoral
famishing	eviscerated	commensal	vagaries
symbiotic	conjecture	deprivation	bereft

Directions: Each sentence below contains an antonym or synonym of a vocabulary word in the box above. Write the correct related vocabulary word in the provided space, and circle all antonyms.

1. Destitute as he was, the sailor never gave up hope that rescuers would find him.

   ____

2. The gaunt faces stared through the prison cell bars, frightening the new guard.

   ____

3. Amy seethed in anger over the complete lack of help from her friends.

   ____

4. The sudden rain created a heavenly rainbow across the rolling plains.

   ____

5. Michael's assumption was way off base, and he apologized for his mistake.

   ____

6. The young boy's reverent attitude during the ceremony angered his parents.

   ____

7. Through their cooperative effort, Lupe and Marta won first prize in the science fair.

   ____

8. No one could shake Abigail from her principled stance against eating meat.

   ____

9. The dog's starving eyes begged for his daily bowl of food. ____________________

10. The abandoned house lay gutted and empty at the end of the dirt road.

    ____

11. The senator's detrimental friendship with the criminal forced him to resign.

    ____

12. The stock market's fluctuations made Juan too nervous to invest his money.

    ____

Name ______________________________

Vocabulary by Association

surreptitiously	pliable	ruminants	feral
scimitars	factuality	reprieve	bestial
impressionistic	unparalleled		

Directions: Define and associate five of the vocabulary words above with characters from *Life of Pi*. On the lines below, explain why that word matches your chosen character. You may associate more than one word with a character but no more than three words per character.

Word #1: __________________

Explanation: ____

____

____

Word #2: __________________

Explanation: ____

____

____

Word #3: __________________

Explanation: ____

____

____

Word #4: __________________

Explanation: ____

____

____

Word #5: __________________

Explanation: ____

____

____

Name ______________________________

Directions: On a separate sheet of paper, write a brief answer to each question as you read the novel at home or in class. Use the questions to guide your reading, prepare for class discussions, and review for quizzes and tests.

Author's Note–Chapter 14

1. Why did the narrator travel to India?
2. Whom does the narrator meet in India, and what does this person tell him?
3. How did Pi improve his life after his journey "left [him] sad and gloomy" (p. 3)?
4. Why does Pi love Canada?
5. What happens the first time Pi eats in an Indian restaurant in Canada?
6. What did Pi's father do before owning a zoo? How does this compare with running a zoo?
7. How is a zoo enclosure the perfect place to give an animal all of its basic needs?
8. What is the most dangerous animal in the zoo, and how does Pi's father demonstrate this to visitors?
9. How does Pi's father demonstrate to his sons the dangers of underestimating animals in the zoo?
10. Why must a lion tamer enter the ring first? What else must a lion tamer remember?
11. Why would a lion tamer prefer to work with a lion of low social rank?

Chapters 15–36

1. To which religion does Pi belong first and foremost, and why is it important to him?
2. Why is Munnar important to Pi, and what is symbolic about the "three hills" within Munnar?
3. What does Pi think of the priest's story about Christianity's origins?
4. What effect does watching the Muslim baker pray have on Pi?
5. How do Mr. Kumar the teacher and Mr. Kumar the baker each directly affect Pi's life?
6. Why do three religious leaders visit Pi, and what do they tell his parents?
7. What two special requests does Pi have for his parents?
8. Why does Pi's family move?
9. What is zoomorphism?
10. How do Ravi and Pi initially feel about leaving India?
11. When and from where does Pi's family leave India, and how do they travel?

Name ______________________________

Chapters 37–52

1. How does Pi rescue Richard Parker? Why does he soon rethink his actions?
2. What does Pi see that makes him realize something is very wrong with the ship?
3. How do "fear and reason" battle in Pi's mind as he hides from Richard Parker?
4. Who is Orange Juice, and how does she arrive on the lifeboat?
5. What is the last thing Pi sees of the ship?
6. Why is the ecosystem on the lifeboat "baffling" to Pi?
7. What message does Pi give the sea turtle?
8. What happens that makes Pi love and admire Orange Juice?
9. How did Richard Parker get his name?
10. When Pi searches the boat, for what specifically does he look?
11. According to Pi's math, how long will the food and water in the locker last him?

Chapters 53–65

1. What does Pi do about the threat Richard Parker poses?
2. What two things save Pi from Richard Parker's advance?
3. What are the six plans Pi devises to deal with Richard Parker?
4. What does Pi realize about his sixth plan? What new plan does Pi devise?
5. What does Pi think about fear?
6. After reading the survival guide, what does Pi realize he must do?
7. What is significant about the cockroach?
8. What does Pi discover about the sea below him?
9. Why does Pi cry after he catches the flying fish?
10. What does the lifeboat resemble to Pi, and why?
11. According to Pi, how long does he drift in the Pacific? Who else drifts nearly as long?
12. What nautical skill does Pi attempt to learn, and what is the end result?

Name ______________________________

Chapters 66–86

1. How does Pi find himself with more food than he can possibly eat?
2. Why did Pi shudder as a boy when he ate bananas?
3. Describe Pi's sleeping habits versus Richard Parker's.
4. What distinct smell does Pi remember from this time?
5. How long must Pi continue to train Richard Parker?
6. How are turtles vital to Pi's plan to train Richard Parker?
7. How is being a castaway like perpetually being in the center of a circle?
8. What is a constant source of anxiety for Pi?
9. In what ways does Pi become an animal?
10. What is significant about the last orange whistle?
11. Why are the birds disappointing to Pi?
12. How does the bolt of lightning affect Pi and Richard Parker?
13. What does Pi promise to Richard Parker after the oil tanker nearly kills them?

Chapters 87–93

1. What is one of Pi's favorite "methods of escape"?
2. What does Pi write about in the final days of his journal?
3. What makes Pi pity Richard Parker, and what happens to Pi's own physical state?
4. Why does Pi find the voice he hears "disgusting"?
5. What does the Frenchman try to do to Pi, and why doesn't he succeed?
6. Why is the island such an "exceptional botanical discovery"?
7. What sources of food do Pi and Richard Parker find on the island?
8. Why does Pi decide to leave the island?
9. Why doesn't Pi leave Richard Parker on the island?
10. What happens to the algae Pi secures to the boat with rope?

Name ______________________________

Chapters 94–100

1. What does Richard Parker do when the lifeboat lands in Mexico? How does this make Pi feel?
2. Who visits Pi, and what are their jobs? Why do they want to speak with him?
3. How do the two men react to Pi's story about traveling with Richard Parker?
4. How does Pi prove his story about Orange Juice's arrival on the boat?
5. Why are the men doubtful that the Frenchman exists?
6. How does Pi respond to the men's statement that all stories have an "element of invention"?
7. How are the animals in Pi's first story represented in the second story?
8. What does Pi tell the two men about the crew of the *Tsimtsum*?
9. After Pi finishes the second story, what does he ask the two men?

Name ______________________________

Feelings

Directions: Complete the chart below to analyze Pi's feelings.

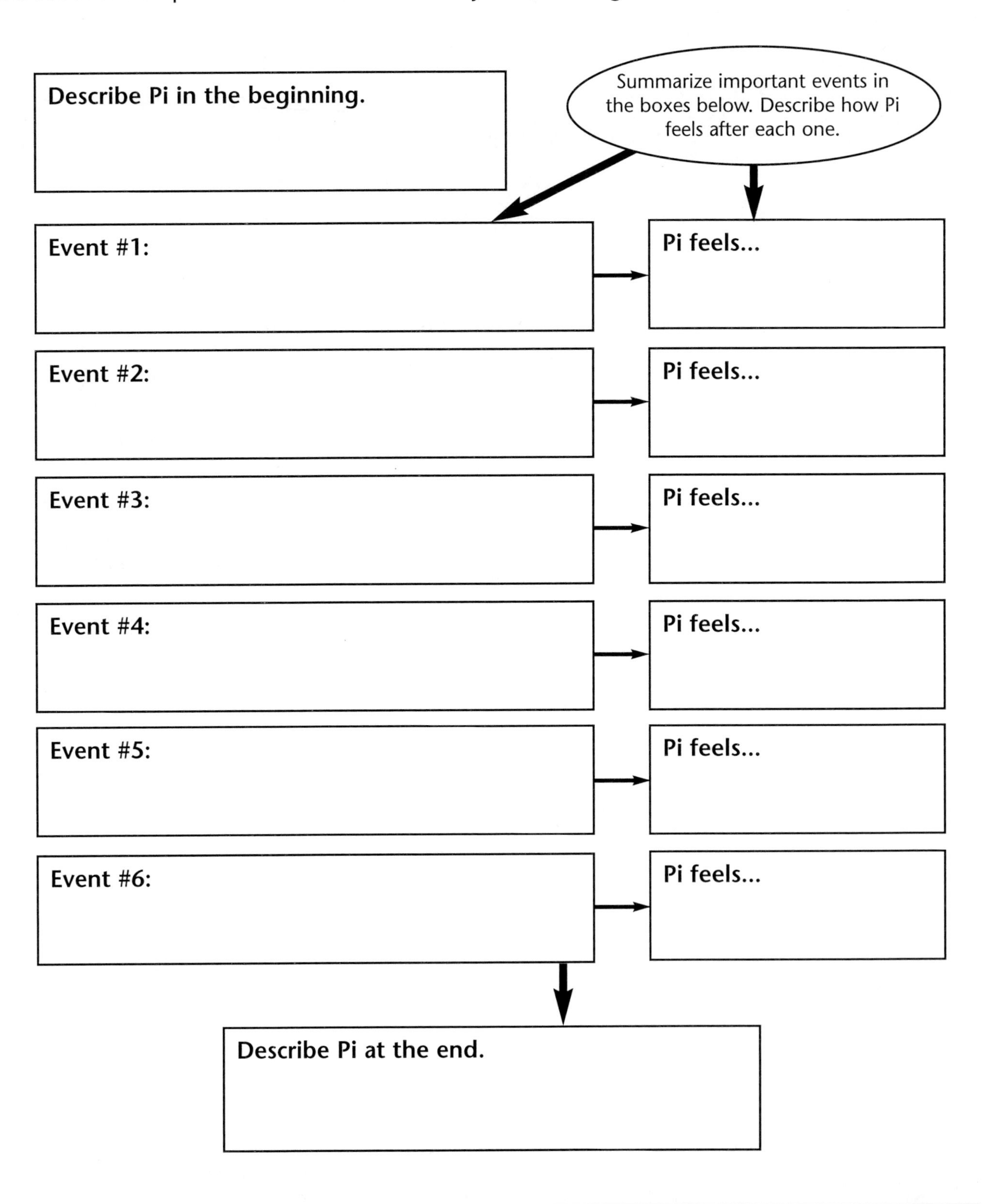

Name ______________________________

Sociogram

Directions: A sociogram shows the relationship between characters in a story. Complete the sociogram below by writing a word to describe the relationships between the characters. Remember, relationships go both ways, so each line requires a descriptive word.

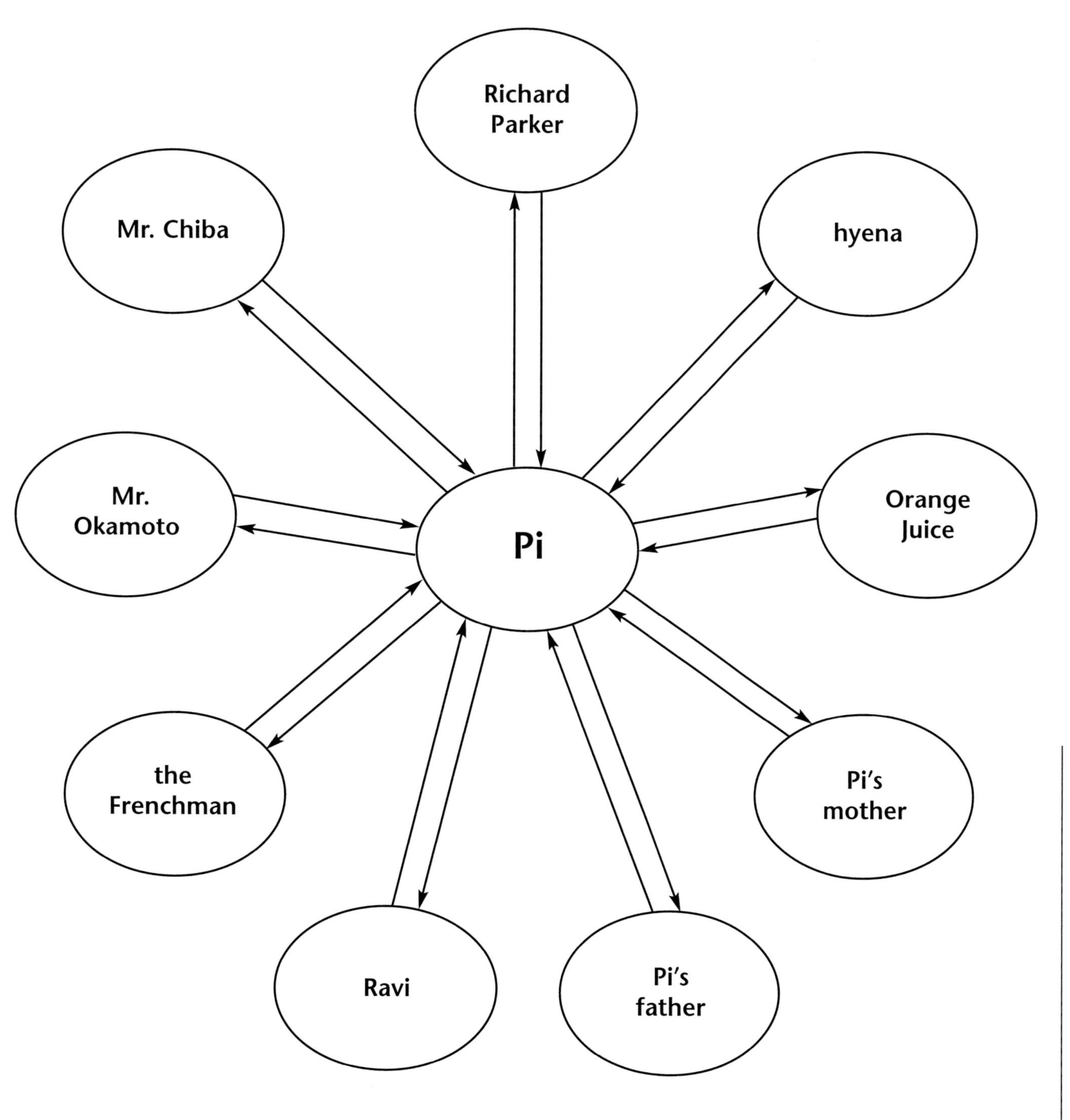

Name ______________________________

Bio-poem

Directions: Using the format below, write a bio-poem about Pi Patel. Then write a bio-poem about yourself using the same format. Write a paragraph describing the values and characteristics you and Pi share.

—Line 1: First name only
—Line 2: Lover of (list three things character loves)
—Line 3: Giver of (list three things character gives)
—Line 4: Needs (list three things character needs)
—Line 5: Wants (list three things character wants)
—Line 6: Is good at (list three things character is good at)
—Line 7: Should work on (list three things character needs to improve)
—Line 8: Is similar to (list three people or other characters to whom this character is similar and list a reason behind each character)
—Line 9: Survivor of (list three things the character survives)
—Line 10: Last name only

Title ______________________________

1. ______________________________
2. ______________________________
3. ______________________________
4. ______________________________
5. ______________________________
6. ______________________________
7. ______________________________
8. ______________________________
9. ______________________________
10. ______________________________

Name ________________________________

Foreshadowing Chart

Foreshadowing is the literary technique of giving clues to coming events in a story.

Directions: What examples of foreshadowing do you recall from the story? If necessary, skim through the chapters to find examples of foreshadowing. List at least four examples below. Explain what clues are given, and then list the coming event that is suggested.

Foreshadowing	Page #	Clues	Coming Event

Name ______________________________

T-Chart

Directions: In the chart below, explain the positive and negative aspects of having Richard Parker in the lifeboat. How does the tiger affect Pi's journey in positive and negative ways? List and explain at least three examples for each.

Positive	Negative

Name ______________________________

Life of Pi
Activity #15 • Comprehension
Use After Reading
(Sequencing)

Time Line

Directions: In the numbered boxes below, write four main events from the novel in the order they happened. In the larger boxes, describe the event or draw a picture representing the event.

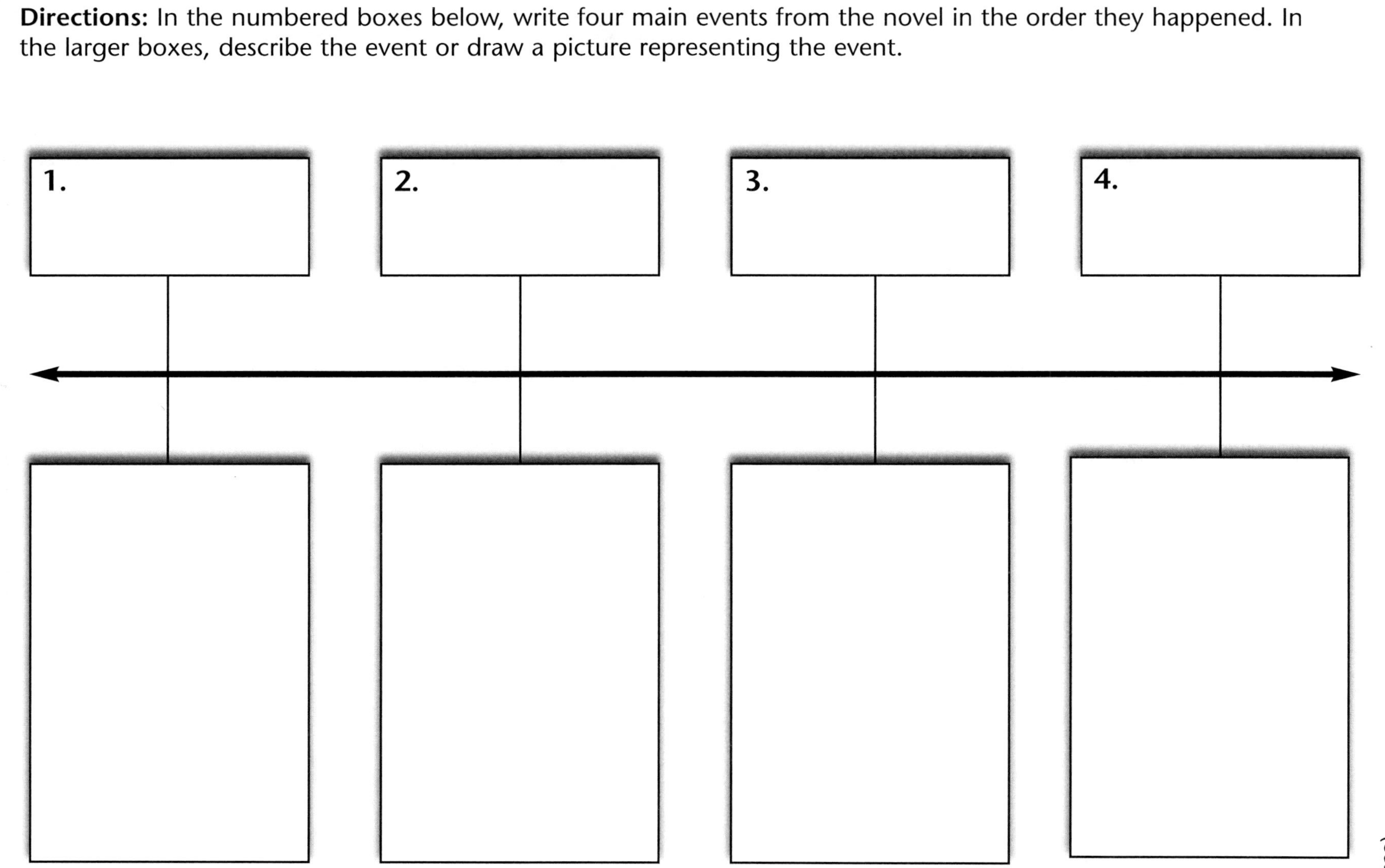

Name ______________________________

Life of Pi
Activity #16 • Literary Analysis
Use After Reading
(Interpret Text)

Using Dialogue

Directions: Choose some dialogue from the novel. Fill in the chart to evaluate the purpose of the dialogue and whether or not it is effective in moving along the plot.

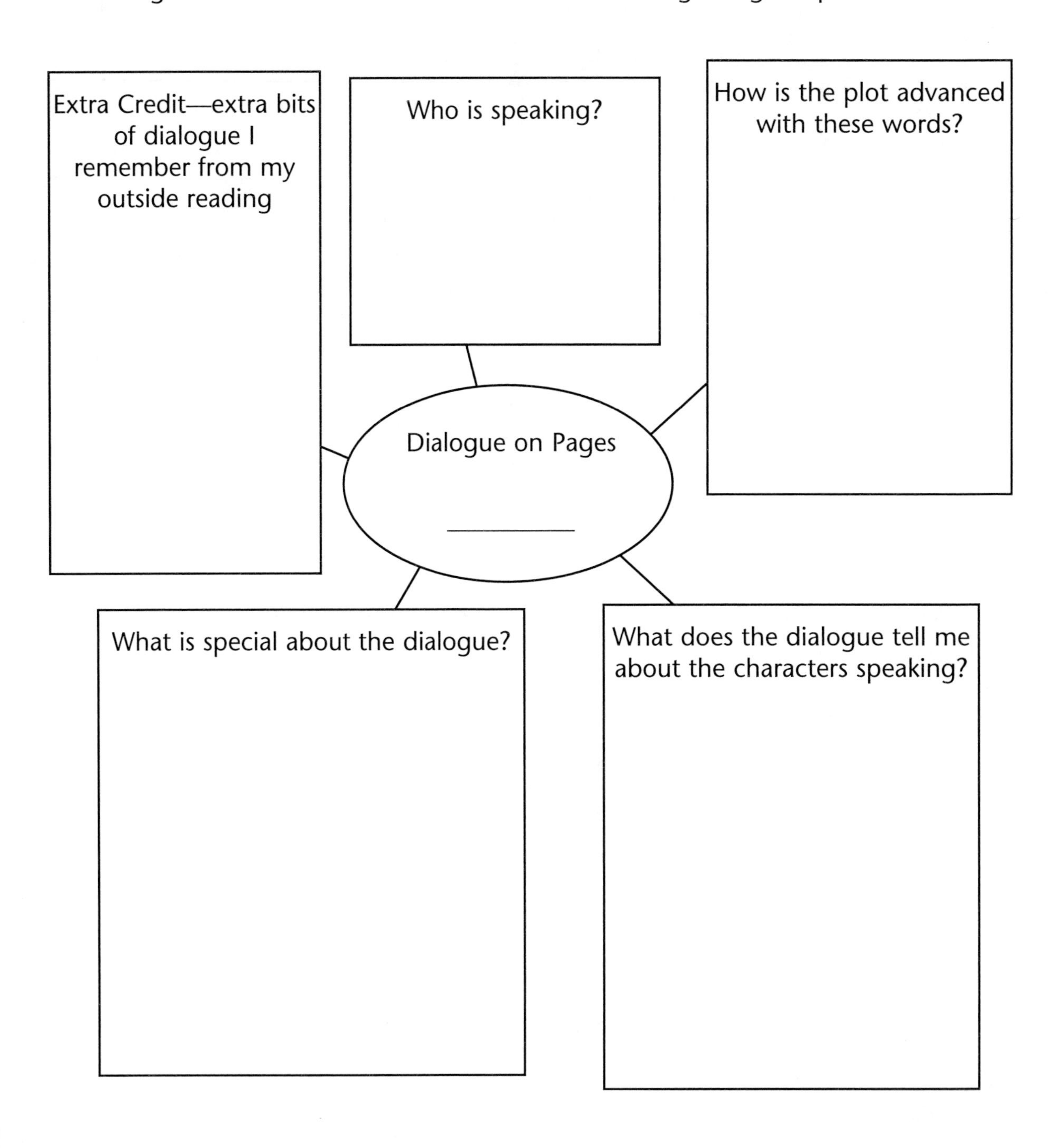

Name ______________________________

Themes and Symbols

Directions: List major themes from the novel in the left column. In the center column, list symbols that you find throughout the novel representing that theme. In the right column, explain briefly how the two relate.

Theme	Symbols	Relationship

Name ______________________________

(Main Idea and Details)
A. True/False: Mark each with a *T* for true or an *F* for false.

____ 1. Socially inferior animals are the most eager to please a trainer.

____ 2. Pi's father posts a sign stating that tigers are the most dangerous animals in the zoo.

____ 3. Pi's teacher, Mr. Kumar, convinces Pi to become an atheist.

____ 4. Canada is a cold, lonely country, and Pi aches to return to India.

____ 5. According to Pi, a lion tamer must enter the ring first.

(Main Idea and Details)
B. Fill in the Blanks

6. Pi's father ran a large ______________ in Madras before he got into the ______________ business.
7. Pi's full name is ______________ Molitor ______________, and he is named after a swimming pool in ______________, France.
8. According to Pi, training a lion is a question of ______________ over brawn.
9. Francis Adirubasamy teaches Pi how to ______________.
10. Pi majors in ______________ and ______________ studies when he attends college in Canada.

(Author's Purpose/Point of View)
C. Open-Ended Comprehension: On the lines below, explain why the narrator goes to India and discuss what he finds there.

____

____

____

____

____

____

____

____

Name ______________________________

Life of Pi
Quiz #2
Chapters 15–36

(Summarize Major Ideas)
A. Short Answer: Write brief answers to the following questions.

1. What fills Pi's house in Canada, and why?

   ____

2. Why is Hinduism important to Pi's development?

   ____

3. Why doesn't Pi understand Father Martin's story of Christianity?

   ____

4. According to Pi, why do people move from one place to another?

   ____

5. Why does Pi's family decide to move?

   ____

(Main Idea and Details)
B. True/False: Mark each with a *T* for true or an *F* for false.

____ 6. Pi's father sold most of his animals to zoos in China.

____ 7. Pi's father argues that different religions have nothing in common.

____ 8. Pi is nervous to enter the church because of Christianity's reputation for severity.

____ 9. Pi argues that forcing him to choose only one religion is against the law.

____ 10. Ravi is excited to go to Canada because the game cricket is popular there.

(Inferences/Character Analysis)
C. Open-Ended Comprehension: On the lines below, explain why Pi feels he can belong to more than one religion at a time.

____

____

____

____

____

____

____

Name ______________________________

(Main Idea and Details)

A. Fill in the Blanks

1. Pi saves ______________ ______________ by throwing him a lifebuoy and calling him toward the boat.
2. The ______________ is the first animal on the lifeboat to be killed.
3. Pi wakes up when he hears a(n) ______________.
4. ______________ ______________ shows great courage in the face of the hyena's attack.
5. ______________ is the mother of invention.

(Character Analysis)

B. Identification: Match each character with the correct description.

____ 6.	Orange Juice	a.	is very crafty; will eat nearly anything
____ 7.	Richard Parker	b.	makes Pi's heart melt with admiration
____ 8.	Pi	c.	is too sleepy to explore the ship
____ 9.	Ravi	d.	silently hides under the tarpaulin
____ 10.	the hyena	e.	buys a map of the world for the trip

(Summarize Major Ideas)

C. Open-Ended Comprehension: On the lines below, explain the effect Richard Parker has on the animals aboard the lifeboat.

____

____

____

____

____

____

____

____

____

____

Name ______________________________

Life of Pi
Quiz #4
Chapters 53–65

(Summarize Major Ideas)
A. Short Answer: Write brief answers to the following questions.

1. Why does Pi decide to build a small raft? What does he use?

____

2. What is *prusten*?

____

3. How does Pi's orange whistle become an important tool?

____

4. What does Pi say about fear?

____

5. How is Pi able to acquire water in the middle of the ocean?

____

(Main Idea and Details)
B. True/False: Mark each with a *T* for true or an *F* for false.

____ 6. Pi builds a raft just in time to escape the hyena's attack.

____ 7. Pi uses leather for bait but fails to catch a fish this way.

____ 8. The survival guide says jellyfish are edible.

____ 9. The survival guide says to go swimming daily.

____ 10. Learning navigation skills is useless to Pi.

(Summarize Major Ideas)
C. Open-Ended Comprehension: On the lines below, explain each plan Pi considers to help him deal with Richard Parker.

____

____

____

____

____

____

____

____

Name ______________________________

(Main Idea and Details)

A. True/False: Mark each with a *T* for true or an *F* for false.

____ 1. After some time aboard the lifeboat, Pi becomes a "champion napper."

____ 2. Pi's greatest wish, aside from salvation, is to have a book to read.

____ 3. After he reached civilization again, Pi began adding salt to everything he ate.

____ 4. Life at sea is one of opposites, the worst pair being boredom and terror.

____ 5. Pi will eat fish but refuses to eat sea turtles.

(Character Analysis)

B. Identification: Read each event below. If it applies to Pi, write *P*. If it applies to Richard Parker, write *R*.

____ 6. is wounded by a mako shark

____ 7. is delighted by a bolt of lightning

____ 8. cannot sleep for more than an hour at a time

____ 9. hides his feces out of respect

____10. stares steadily at the hand flares as they hiss to life

(Summarize Major Ideas)

C. Open-Ended Comprehension: On the lines below, explain exactly how Pi practices his many faiths while at sea.

____

____

____

____

____

____

____

____

____

____

____

Name ______________________________

Life of Pi
Quiz #6
Chapters 87–93

(Main Idea and Details)

A. Fill in the Blanks

1. Pi finds a ______________ in the trash, and he uses it to send a(n) ______________ back into the sea.
2. The voice has a(n) ______________ accent, and the owner of the voice admits that he is also lost and ______________.
3. Although there are trees on the island, there is no anchoring ______________, just thick tubes of ______________.
4. To Pi's surprise, there are ______________ ponds on the island, many of them containing ______________ to eat.
5. Pi finds ______________ ______________ in a tree and realizes that he must leave the island.

(Summarize Major Ideas)

B. Short Answer: Write brief answers to the following questions.

6. Why is Pi upset when Richard Parker mauls the Frenchman?

____

7. Why does Richard Parker return to the boat every night?

____

8. Why does Pi allow Richard Parker on the boat when he leaves the island?

____

9. Aside from being made of algae, how is the island not an island?

____

10. Why is it ironic that Pi finds the island after coming so close to dying?

____

Name ______________________________

(Interpret Text/Theme)

C. Open-Ended Comprehension: On the lines below, explain the following statement: "The lower you are, the higher your mind will want to soar" (p. 358).

____

____

____

____

____

____

____

____

____

____

____

____

____

____

____

____

____

Name ______________________________

(Main Idea and Details)
A. True/False: Mark each with a *T* for true or an *F* for false.

____ 1. Mr. Okamoto thinks Pi is hiding details about how the ship sank.

____ 2. Landing on the beach is very difficult, and the lifeboat almost capsizes.

____ 3. Mr. Okamoto and Mr. Chiba drive all the way from California to see Pi.

____ 4. Pi thinks the crew members released the zoo animals right before the ship sank.

____ 5. Pi thinks the officers of the ship were warm and friendly to him and his family.

(Main Idea and Details)
B. Fill in the Blanks

6. The two men don't believe Pi's story about ____________ ____________'s survival because they don't think ____________ can float.
7. Mr. Okamoto works for the ____________ Department in the ____________ Ministry of Transport.
8. The two men say they don't want a story with ____________, but a story with just "straight ____________."
9. The Frenchman was the ____________ aboard the ship, and he shares many of the same character traits with the ____________.
10. The two men prefer the ____________ story, the one with ____________, because it seems less horrific.

(Character Analysis)
C. Open-Ended Comprehension: On the lines below, explain why Pi is devastated by Richard Parker's departure.

____

____

____

____

____

____

____

____

Name ______________________________

(Character Analysis)

A. Identification: Match each character with the correct description.

____ 1.	Ravi	a.	a baker and Sufi mystic
____ 2.	the hyena	b.	is ill-prepared for his first trip to India
____ 3.	Pi	c.	a fan of cricket, movies, and music
____ 4.	Mr. Kumar	d.	tends to drool; earns Pi's deepest respect
____ 5.	Pi's father	e.	acquires his name through a clerical error
____ 6.	Pi's mother	f.	says separate religions have nothing in common
____ 7.	the narrator	g.	studies the three-toed sloth in college
____ 8.	Richard Parker	h.	defends Pi's desire to be baptized
____ 9.	Orange Juice	i.	known to Pi as Mamaji
____ 10.	Francis Adirubasamy	j.	crafty; will eat almost anything

B. Multiple Choice: Choose the BEST answer.

(Main Idea and Details)

____ 11. What is the name of the ship that sinks?

(a) *Tezpur*
(b) *Tierra*
(c) *Tsimtsum*
(d) *Tsonga*

(Setting)

____ 12. In which Indian city does Pi's father own a zoo?

(a) Madras
(b) Munnar
(c) Palanpur
(d) Pondicherry

Name ______________________________

(Main Idea and Details)

____ 13. Richard Parker's original name was supposed to be

(a) Bengal
(b) Prowler
(c) Thirsty
(d) Vishnu

(Theme)

____ 14. What is life's "only true opponent," according to Pi?

(a) fear
(b) Man
(c) religion
(d) starvation

(Point of View)

____ 15. Pi considers the blind Frenchman to be his

(a) brother
(b) enemy
(c) father
(d) savior

(Conflict/Resolution)

____ 16. What fatal plan does Pi abandon in order to train Richard Parker so they may co-exist?

(a) choke him
(b) war of wits
(c) poison him
(d) war of attrition

Name ______________________________

(Main Idea and Details)

____ 17. What kind of story does Mr. Okamoto want from Pi?

(a) one with animals

(b) one with invention

(c) one about Pi's family

(d) one with only straight facts

(Main Idea and Details)

____ 18. What religion does Pi discover in the hills of Munnar?

(a) Christianity

(b) Hinduism

(c) Islam

(d) Taoism

(Cause/Effect)

____ 19. Why does Pi leave the island of algae?

(a) He hopes to reach Mexico.

(b) He fears the Frenchman will find him.

(c) He is afraid Richard Parker will forget his training.

(d) He knows the island is carnivorous and will kill him.

(Point of View)

____ 20. Pi's father believes that Muslims are

(a) admirable

(b) outsiders

(c) overlooked

(d) territorial

Name ______________________________

(Main Idea and Details)

C. Fill in the Blanks

21. Pi's parents never learn to ______________, but Pi learns at a young age.
22. Pi's prized possession while on the lifeboat is a little orange ______________.
23. ______________ ______________ impresses Pi by fighting the hyena.
24. Pi is a ______________, finding it very difficult to eat meat, but after a long time at sea, he eats like a(n) ______________.
25. Ravi likes to use the phrase "______________ beckons," but he is too sleepy to investigate the ship with Pi.
26. Pi tells Mr. Okamoto, "If you stumble at mere ______________, what are you living for? Isn't ______________ hard to believe?"
27. Richard Parker spends most of his time napping underneath the ______________.
28. Pi asks the two men if there is anything about his second story that they would like him to ______________.
29. The island is made of ______________ and has countless ______________ living in its trees and vegetation.
30. Pi believes that "all religions are ______________," and he just wants to "______________ God."

Name ______________________________

D. Open-Ended Short Answer: In two to three sentences each, answer two of the following on a separate sheet of paper.

(Literary Devices/Point of View)
(a) Explain why Pi is an "unreliable narrator."

(Literary Devices/Theme)
(b) Explain the term anthropomorphism as it applies to the novel.

(Cause/Effect)
(c) Explain why Pi doesn't leave Richard Parker on the algae island.

(Character Analysis)
(d) Explain why Pi cries when he arrives in Mexico.

E. Essay: Complete one of the following in a well-developed essay. Cite specific evidence from the novel to support your answer.

(Making Connections/Support Responses)
(a) Which story do you believe is true, Pi's first tale with Richard Parker, or the second story with no animals at all? Cite three pieces of evidence to support your choice.

(Character Analysis/Support Responses)
(b) Richard Parker is the genuine hero of the novel, regardless of which story is authentic. Assume this statement is true, and support it with evidence from the novel.

(Main Idea and Details/Theme)
(c) Explain how Pi is able to train Richard Parker. What key elements are important to Pi's success?

Answer Key

Activity #1: 1. Yann Martel 2. Answers will vary but could include that the book is a narrative or possibly a biography or autobiography. 3. 2001 4. 401 5.–6. Answers will vary.

Activity #2: Answers will vary.

Activity #3: 1. a 2. d 3. c 4. a 5. b 6. a 7. a 8. b 9. b 10. d 11. a 12. d

Activity #4: Answers will vary. Example: petulant: Definition—ill-tempered or sullen in a childish manner; Synonyms—grouchy, irritable, snobbish; Antonyms—charming, delightful, carefree; Part of Speech—adjective; Pronunciation—pet·u·lant [péchələnt]; Sentence—The man's *petulant* attitude caused everyone to leave the party early.

Activities #5–#6: Answers will vary.

Activity #7:

												[1]T		[2]H						
								[3]H		[4]F	O	R	B	E	A	R	A	N	C	E
								I				A		I						
								L				N		N						
			[5]A					L				S		O						
			R					O				L		U						
			C					C				U		S						
			H					K				C								
		[6]M	I	S	C	O	N	S	T	R	U	E		[7]M						
			P									N		A						
			E									[8]T	I	L	A	K	S			
[9]E	X	A	L	T	E	D								A						
			A					[10]G	R	E	G	A	R	I	O	U	S			
			G											S						
			O										[11]P	E	N	D	U	L	U	M

Activity #8: 1. Destitute/Bereft 2. gaunt/emaciated 3. lack/deprivation 4. heavenly/infernal 5. assumption/conjecture 6. reverent/sacrilegious 7. cooperative/symbiotic 8. principled/amoral 9. starving/famishing 10. gutted/eviscerated 11. detrimental/commensal 12. fluctuations/vagaries; Antonyms—4, 6, 8, 11

Activity #9: Associations will vary. Example: scimitars—Richard Parker; The tiger's sharp claws are like these sharp-bladed weapons.

Study Guide

Author's Note–Chapter 14: 1. to finish his novel in a place where he can stretch his money and to ease his restlessness 2. Francis Adirubasamy, an old family friend; He says he has a story for the narrator that will "make [him] believe in God" (p. *ix*). 3. by focusing his attention on his spiritual development and his academic career (zoology and religious studies) 4. It is filled with compassionate, intelligent people, and anyway, he has nothing to go home to in India. 5. Pi begins to eat with his fingers, but a waiter mocks his behavior. Ashamed, he wipes his hands and eats with utensils. 6. He was a hotelkeeper; The animals in the zoo are the worst possible "hotel guests" because they never leave their rooms, demand a constant supply of food, have dirty, noisy visitors, and the rooms need constant cleaning. 7. In a zoo enclosure, an animal will find food, a watering hole, a place to sleep, a place to bathe and groom, and there is no need to hunt or fear predators. 8. Man is the most dangerous "animal" in the zoo, and Pi's father shows this by placing a sign by the entrance saying, "DO YOU KNOW WHICH IS THE MOST DANGEROUS ANIMAL IN THE ZOO?" (pp. 38–39) and placing a mirror next to the sign. 9. Pi's father makes the boys watch a tiger kill a goat, and then he takes the boys around the zoo and explains how each animal could potentially kill them. 10. so that the lions know they are entering his territory; He must shout, snap his whip, keep erect posture, a steady gaze, a calm demeanor, a firm first step, and make the lions realize that he is the dominant male. 11. Lions with low social rank are more amenable and eager to please. They seek protection from the alpha, or the trainer.

Chapters 15–36: 1. He is a Hindu first. It is important to him because Hinduism is the original landscape of his religious imagination. 2. Munnar is where Pi discovers Christianity. The three hills in Munnar each house a religious building belonging to Christians, Hindus, and Muslims. They symbolize Pi's religious awakening to all faiths. 3. Pi thinks it is "a downright weird story" (p. 67) and cannot understand the psychology of a God who would sacrifice himself for mankind. 4. Pi finds this prayer ritual "quick, necessary, physical, muttered, striking" (p. 76). He thinks of this ritual while he prays in the Christian church. 5. They teach Pi about biology and Islam and inspire him to study zoology and religious studies when he attends the University of Toronto. They are "the prophets of [his] Indian youth" (p. 78). 6. They have heard Pi is practicing different religions simultaneously. They say Pi must choose only one. 7. Pi wants a Muslim prayer rug and a Christian baptism. 8. Pi's family decides to move to Canada when political unrest makes life in India unsatisfactory. 9. when an animal thinks a different animal or a human is one of its own kind 10. Just like the animals, Pi and Ravi also feel as though they are being sold and shipped to Canada against their will. 11. They leave Madras on June 21st, 1977, on a cargo ship called the *Tsimtsum.*

Chapters 37–52: 1. Pi blows a whistle and throws a lifebuoy and rope to Richard Parker to help him stay afloat. Pi doesn't realize what he has done until it is too late. 2. Pi notices that the lifeboat isn't hanging straight, that the boat is tilted, and that he can look over the side of the boat and see the ship's black side instead of the sea. 3. Pi fears Richard Parker will jump through the tarpaulin and kill him. Reason tells Pi that the tarpaulin is strong, that Richard Parker won't jump right through without any warning, and that Richard Parker can't see him. 4. Orange Juice is a Borneo orang-utan from the family's zoo, and she arrives floating on a bundle of bananas. 5. a patch of oil on the surface of the water 6. Pi doesn't understand why the hyena has not attacked and killed Orange Juice. While the two would not have met naturally in the wild, they must be able to sense their predator-prey relationship. However, Orange Juice sits with her back to the hyena, and the hyena does not attack. 7. to tell a ship where Pi is 8. Orange Juice hits the hyena on the head after he attacks her. 9. Richard Parker got his name in a clerical mix-up. A hunter named Richard Parker captured and named a baby tiger Thirsty, but the papers accidentally switched the hunter's and baby tiger's names. 10. a storage locker filled with food, water, and supplies 11. He has enough food for 93 days and enough water to last 124 days.

Chapters 53–65: 1. To ensure his safety from Richard Parker, Pi builds a small raft out of life jackets and floatable oars so he can float away from the lifeboat. 2. Richard Parker finds his footing awkward on the tarpaulin. Also, Pi throws the tiger a rat as a sort of "peace offering." 3. Plan Number One: Push him off the lifeboat. Plan Number Two: Kill him with the six morphine syringes. Plan Number Three: Attack him with all available weaponry. Plan Number Four: Choke him. Plan Number Five: Poison him, set him on fire, electrocute him. Plan

Number Six: Wage a war of attrition. 4. Pi can never outlive the tiger; Pi resolves to keep the tiger alive. 5. Pi says fear is "life's only true opponent" (p. 203) and only fear can defeat life. Fear is an awful emotion that goes for your weakest spot, and it has no decency. One by one, fear overcomes all of your emotions, thoughts, defenses, and your body. 6. Pi realizes he must start training Richard Parker. He must also start fishing, find a way to shelter himself, secure the lifeboat with a second rope, improve the raft, and stop hoping that rescue will come. 7. The cockroach is the last life form on the boat aside from Richard Parker and Pi. Pi is saddened to know that of the many animals that began the journey, only he and Richard Parker remain. 8. Pi discovers that there is a city of life below him, filled with highways and streets of fish in great glimmering streams. The possibilities for food are endless. 9. Pi knows he must kill the fish to eat, but he has never killed anything before. Taking another life, even to save his own, is an awful experience for Pi. 10. It resembles a zoo enclosure because the sea forces Richard Parker to stay in his territory where he has his own shelter, food supply, watering hole, and a lookout. 11. Pi spends 227 days drifting. The next longest was a Korean merchant sailor named Poon who drifted for 173 days in the 1950s. 12. Pi tries to teach himself navigation. He eventually gives up because he has no means of controlling where he is going, so the skill would be useless.

Chapters 66–86: 1. Pi becomes such a successful hunter that he quickly runs out of space to store all the fish and turtle meat he captures and cures. 2. The sound of bananas snapping open sounded like a neck snapping. 3. Pi rests often but rarely sleeps. Richard Parker, however, becomes a "champion napper," and sleeps for most of the day and night. 4. the smell of the spent hand-flare shells 5. Pi must continue to train Richard Parker "until the association in the animal's mind between the sound of the whistle and the feeling of intense, incapacitating nausea is fixed and totally unambiguous" (p. 259). 6. Pi uses turtle shells for shields during Richard Parker's training. 7. A castaway is constantly surrounded by the same circle of never-ending water. Pi says, "Your gaze is always a radius" (p. 272). 8. the lack of fresh water 9. Pi learns to kill and eat like an animal, wolfing down his prey in order to sate his appetite quickly. 10. The whistle is all that remains between Pi and death—it is all Pi has to make Richard Parker obey. 11. Pi keeps hoping sightings of birds will indicate land, but they never do. 12. Pi is "dazed" and "thunderstruck," but not afraid. Pi thinks the lightning bolt is a miracle. Richard Parker, however, is terrified and hides in the bottom of the boat. 13. Pi promises that he will save Richard Parker and get him to land.

Chapters 87–93: 1. He puts a wet rag over his face, which asphyxiates him and causes him to dream long, vivid dreams. Pi enjoys this practice because it makes time go by quickly. 2. Pi writes about his and Richard Parker's deteriorating condition. On the last page, Pi writes that he will die that very day. 3. Pi realizes Richard Parker is going blind. Soon after, Pi also goes blind. 4. While Pi describes vegetarian foods he would like to eat, the voice describes a variety of cooked animal organs and meat dishes. 5. Once aboard Pi's lifeboat, the Frenchman tries to kill Pi. Once the Frenchman steps into Richard Parker's lair, the tiger rises up and mauls him. 6. There are trees on the island, but no soil or sand. The entire island is made of edible algae tubes that are sweet on the outside and salty on the inside. 7. The island itself is edible, but there are also thousands of meerkats that supply Pi and Richard Parker with plenty of meat. There are also freshwater pools on the island where dead fish appear, supplying them with even more food. 8. He finds human teeth in a tree and discovers that the island is carnivorous. 9. Pi can't stand the thought of leaving his only companion to be eaten by the island. 10. At night, the algae turns acidic and burns through the rope holding it.

Chapters 94–100: 1. Richard Parker immediately leaps from the boat and disappears into the jungle. This breaks Pi's heart because there is no goodbye between him and his friend. 2. Mr. Tomohiro Okamoto and Mr. Atsuro Chiba both work for the Maritime Department in the Japanese Ministry of Transport. They wish to speak to Pi about the sinking of the *Tsimtsum,* since he is the only survivor. 3. The men are slightly offended and think that Pi considers them fools. They think his story has many holes. 4. To prove that Orange Juice could have floated on a bushel of bananas, Pi asks the men to float a banana in the sink. 5. The men find it very doubtful that two blind humans drifting in separate lifeboats in the Pacific would meet. 6. Pi says that any story has elements of invention. Simply understanding something is a form of invention, so life itself is invention. 7. In the first story, Pi shares the lifeboat with a tiger, a hyena, a zebra, and an orang-utan. In the second tale, the hyena is represented by the Frenchman, the orang-utan is represented by Pi's mother, and the zebra is represented by the wounded Chinese sailor. Richard Parker is represented by Pi, who attacks and kills the Frenchman after his murderous deeds. 8. Pi tells them that the crew members were unfriendly, sullen, drunk, and unfit to properly man the ship. The officers were only slightly better. 9. Pi asks them if they like the story, if they believe it, and if there is anything they would like him to change.

Note: Answers to Activities #10–#17 will vary. Suggested responses are given where applicable.

Activity #10: Pi in the beginning: Pi is a curious, intelligent, gentle young man; Event #1: Pi watches a tiger eat a goat in his father's zoo—Pi feels terrified; Event #2: Pi watches Mr. Kumar perform a Muslim ritual—Pi feels awe; Event #3: Members of three different churches confront Pi about his religious choices—Pi feels embarrassed yet earnest; Event #4: Pi sees Richard Parker sinking immediately after the ship sinks—Pi feels desperate; Event #5: Pi kills the flying fish in the blanket—Pi feels shame and regret; Event #6: Pi finds human teeth in the tree—Pi feels repulsion and shock; Pi at the end: Pi has become an experienced, responsible, and more spiritual adult.

Activity #11: Suggestions—Pi to Richard Parker—wary; Richard Parker to Pi—deferential; Pi to hyena—appalled; hyena to Pi—dismissive; Pi to Orange Juice—admiring; Orange Juice to Pi—oblivious; Pi to his mother—appreciative; Pi's mother to Pi—affectionate; Pi to his father—respectful; Pi's father to Pi—instructional; Pi to Ravi—tolerant; Ravi to Pi—mocking; Pi to the Frenchman—inviting; the Frenchman to Pi—calculating; Pi to Mr. Okamoto—polite; Mr. Okamoto to Pi—disbelieving; Pi to Mr. Chiba—entertaining; Mr. Chiba to Pi—bewildered

Activity #12: Suggestions—Line 1: Pi; Line 2: Lover of God, life, family; Line 3: Giver of peace, information, love; Line 4: Needs human contact, food, water; Line 5: Wants a book, a real goodbye, his family back; Line 6: Is good at understanding animals, fishing, survival; Line 7: Should work on his ability to read others, not trusting everyone, staying on topic during an interview; Line 8: Is similar to Robinson Crusoe (both castaways), Richard Parker (both animalistic), and his father (both fair and firm); Line 9: Survivor of the sinking of the *Tsimtsum,* a carnivorous island, living with Richard Parker; Line 10: Patel

Activity #13: Suggestion—Foreshadowing: Pi will confront an infinite presence that will define his life; Page #: 28; Clues: Pi decides to change his name from Piscine Patel (which is a pool in France) to Pi, like the mathematic symbol which is symbolic of an infinite numeric sequence. The Pacific seems like an infinite body of water while Pi is floating in the lifeboat, much like the symbol he names himself after, which is very different from a small pool, where his original name comes from; Coming Event—Pi will face the infinite in both God and in his trip across the infinite waters of the Pacific.

Activity #14: Suggestions—Positive: Richard Parker offers companionship, is built-in protection, and gives Pi a purpose to survive; Negative: Richard Parker's presence is a constant threat, the tiger kills and claims everything else initially on the lifeboat, and another boat might be hesitant to rescue a boy sharing a boat with a tiger.

Activities #15–#16: Answers will vary.

Activity #17: Suggestion—Theme: the value and significance of water; Symbols: Pi's swim teacher (Mamaji), Pi's full name (Piscine, or swimming pool), Pi's baptism, the Pacific Ocean, rationing water with Richard Parker; Relationship: Water surrounds Pi throughout the novel. He learns to swim when most others cannot, he is named after a pool in France, he is baptized in water, he feels closest to God when he sees the ocean and once when he sees snow (frozen water) fall from a tree, his thirst for water helps him overcome his fear of Richard Parker and search the boat for a storage locker—an act that likely saves Pi's life, and the ocean itself is both a trove of food and an endless void that taunts him. Pi also proves that Orange Juice came to the lifeboat by asking the men to float a banana in water. Throughout the novel, Pi is constantly connected with water.

Quiz #1: A. 1. T 2. F 3. F 4. F 5. T **B.** 6. hotel/zoo 7. Piscine/Patel/Paris 8. brains 9. swim 10. zoology/religious **C.** Answers will vary. Refer to the scoring rubric on page 43 of this guide.

Quiz #2: A. 1. religious symbols, pictures, and books from many different religions; Pi loves God deeply. 2. It is the original landscape of his religious imagination. 3. He can't understand why a god would suffer or sacrifice for others. 4. in the hopes of a better life 5. Political unrest in India upsets Pi's parents and makes them nervous to stay. **B.** 6. F 7. T 8. T 9. F 10. F **C.** Answers will vary. Refer to the scoring rubric on page 43 of this guide.

Quiz #3: A. 1. Richard Parker 2. zebra 3. explosion 4. Orange Juice 5. Necessity **B.** 6. b 7. d 8. e 9. c 10. a **C.** Answers will vary. Refer to the scoring rubric on page 43 of this guide.

Quiz #4: A. 1. He fears confronting Richard Parker. He uses the life vests, oars, and rope to build his raft. 2. one of the quietest, least aggressive sounds tigers make; It is a sign of "friendliness and harmless intentions" (p. 206). 3. The orange whistle becomes Pi's "whip" for training Richard Parker. 4. Fear is life's only true opponent; it is clever and treacherous and respects nothing about life. 5. by using solar stills, the rain catcher, and his cache of canned water **B.** 6. F 7. T 8. F 9. F 10. T **C.** Answers will vary. Refer to the scoring rubric on page 43 of this guide.

Quiz #5: A. 1. F 2. T 3. F 4. T 5. F **B.** 6. R 7. P 8. P 9. R 10. R **C.** Answers will vary. Refer to the scoring rubric on page 43 of this guide.

Quiz #6: A. 1. bottle/message 2. French/blind 3. soil/algae 4. freshwater/fish 5. human teeth **B.** 6. Pi respects all life, and the loss of a human life simply to save his own is a tragedy to him, especially considering how lonely he is. 7. The island turns acidic and would burn or dissolve human or animal flesh. 8. To leave the tiger would be cruel, as Richard Parker would surely die. Pi cannot leave his only companion behind. 9. The island is free-floating, unattached to any rock or land mass. 10. Right after Pi almost died of thirst, starvation, and strangulation, he finds an island with no predators, fresh water, and plenty of food, but the island itself is toxic and will kill him if he stays, so he must leave again. **C.** Answers will vary. Refer to the scoring rubric on page 43 of this guide.

Quiz #7: A. 1. F 2. T 3. T 4. T 5. F **B.** 6. Orange Juice/bananas 7. Maritime/Japanese 8. invention/facts 9. cook/hyena 10. first/animals **C.** Answers will vary. Refer to the scoring rubric on page 43 of this guide.

Novel Test: A. 1. c 2. j 3. g 4. a 5. f 6. h 7. b 8. e 9. d 10. i **B.** 11. c 12. d 13. c 14. a 15. a 16. d 17. d 18. a 19. d 20. b **C.** 21. swim 22. whistle 23. Orange Juice 24. vegetarian/animal 25. adventure 26. believability/love (p. 375) 27. tarpaulin 28. change 29. algae/meerkats 30. true/love (p. 87) **D.–E.** Responses will vary. Refer to the scoring rubric on page 43 of this guide.

Linking Novel Units® Student Packets to National and State Reading Assessments

During the past several years, an increasing number of students have faced some form of state-mandated competency testing in reading. Many states now administer state-developed assessments to measure the skills and knowledge emphasized in their particular reading curriculum. This Novel Units® guide includes open-ended comprehension questions that correlate with state-mandated reading assessments. The rubric below provides important information for evaluating responses to open-ended comprehension questions. Teachers may also use scoring rubrics provided for their own state's competency test.

Scoring Rubric for Open-Ended Items

3-Exemplary	Thorough, complete ideas/information Clear organization throughout Logical reasoning/conclusions Thorough understanding of reading task Accurate, complete response
2-Sufficient	Many relevant ideas/pieces of information Clear organization throughout most of response Minor problems in logical reasoning/conclusions General understanding of reading task Generally accurate and complete response
1-Partially Sufficient	Minimally relevant ideas/information Obvious gaps in organization Obvious problems in logical reasoning/conclusions Minimal understanding of reading task Inaccuracies/incomplete response
0-Insufficient	Irrelevant ideas/information No coherent organization Major problems in logical reasoning/conclusions Little or no understanding of reading task Generally inaccurate/incomplete response

Notes

